RIVEREN: MY HOME, OUR COUNTRY
A BANTAM BOOK

First published in Australia and New Zealand in 2000 by Bantam

National Library of Australia
Cataloguing-in-Publication Entry

Underwood, Terry (Marie Thérèse)
Riveren: my home, our country.

ISBN 1 86325 215 0.

1. Ranches – Northern Territory – Riveren Station.
2. Riveren Station (N.T.). 3. Riveren Station (N.T.) – Pictorial works. I. Title.

636.01099429

Transworld Publishers,
a division of Random House Australia Pty Ltd
20 Alfred Street, Milsons Point, NSW 2061

Random House New Zealand Limited
18 Poland Road, Glenfield, Auckland

Transworld Publishers (UK) Limited
61-63 Uxbridge Road, Ealing, London W5 5SA

Random House Inc
1540 Broadway, New York, New York 10036

The author wishes to thank the Northern Territory Department of Lands,
Planning and Environment for the pastoral map of Riveren.
The subtitles of each chapter are from the author's first book,
In the Middle of Nowhere.
Cover design by Liz Seymour
Text design by Liz Seymour
Printed through Phoenix, Hong Kong
Colour separations by Response Colour Graphics, Sydney

10 9 8 7 6 5 4 3 2 1

Foreword

by Daryl Somers

In February 1998 I penned the Foreword to *In the Middle of Nowhere*, my dear friend Terry Underwood's now classic real-life adventure of her pioneering Outback family. In extreme isolation, John and Terry's initial lodgings in the bush made the Swiss Family Robinson's treehouse sound like a luxury five-star pub! Hardback sales of her amazing story sold through the roof – and publishers say you don't sell in volume until you release in paperback!

Only for the incredible bond between two people could this saga of courage and determination, against all odds, prove triumphant. I am truly in awe of this wonderful Australian family and feel so proud to enjoy a special friendship with them. Through great hardship they have raised four salt-of-the-earth children who have inherited the same fierce determination to contribute in their own way to this unique country of ours.

John Underwood was born to this rugged life; I think of him as the John Wayne of Australia. He is a gentle giant of a man who has not only faced the great challenges but has been justly recognised with an A.M. for his enormous contribution to the Australian cattle industry. Of course, as they say, behind every strong man there is a strong woman. Terry has not only fulfilled her role as wife, soulmate, lover, mother and business partner, but contributed other rare gifts: boundless energy, brilliant storytelling (her mum always encouraged the employment of colourful adjectives), an uncanny memory, and indeed a talent for photography (she won a Bulletin Award in 1991). Add to this discipline, organisational skills and a good sense of humour and you have a formidable package.

In all, *Riveren: My Home, Our Country* offers an intimate portrait of life on an Australian cattle station. It is rich and rewarding and glimpses a lifestyle we city slickers can only dream about. One would think to live the life would be hard enough, but to record it photographically is quite extraordinary. I can't help but think if Captain Cook had a camera, would he have recorded his epic journey as exquisitely as Terry Underwood?

DARYL SOMERS
JANUARY 2000

To my parents, Frank
and Elizabeth Augustus,
whose love and goodness
guide me always

Acknowledgements

In 1995 my photographic exhibition entitled The Cattle Kingdom, at the prestigious Barry Stern Gallery in Sydney, included photographs contained herein. Amongst those overwhelmed by the framed but nonetheless powerful lure of the bush was literary agent extraordinaire Selwa Anthony. Selwa's suggestion is now reality: 'First your personal story, Terry, then your photographic book.' Thank you Selwa, my special friend and loyal supporter.

Jude McGee has once again proved a sound ally. I thank also Maggie Hamilton, Shona Martyn, Lisa Hanrahan and the other professional members of my publishing team for facilitating the passions and persistence of this Bush Woman from afar.

To all those others who work the land, thank you for your inspiration. To my beloved family and dear friends — without your love, compassion, support and understanding my life would indeed be bleak. With heartfelt gratitude I acknowledge you all.

RIVEREN STATION

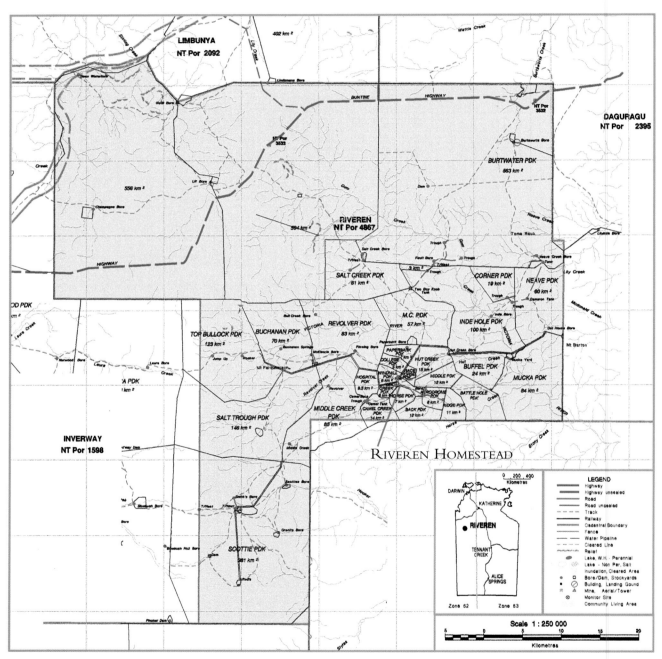

Contents

Introduction

Once I was an outsider.

In 1963 at Sydney's St Vincent's Hospital, I nursed a strapping young stockman from way up north. Not only was his smile big enough to light the universe, but his enthusiastic commitment to a life-style that was totally foreign to me was both puzzling and fascinating. The size of his cattle station home, all 2400 square miles of it, seemed quite incomprehensible, and I could not imagine how anyone lived and survived in such a remote world of wide open spaces.

After he departed Sydney, Big John sent me a postcard. Gradually our intermittent letters became regular, the dears changed to darlings, and after two whole years I realised it was time to reassess our friendship. With my younger brother in tow as the family-appointed chaperone, I boarded a plane for the very first time and flew for two days across the unbelievable vastness of inland Australia to seek some answers.

I remember so vividly those first impressions. How overwhelming was the absolute desolation, impenetrable vastness, blistering heat, ferocious flies, relentless glare – and the drought, the drought, the drought. How overpowering was the tenacity of those who carved out their existence in that wilderness, always with indomitable spirit. I listened, I looked, but did not always see what I was looking at. How could I understand? I was an outsider.

It has been said that we choose those we like; with those we love we have no say in the matter. Hundreds of letters and three years later, the Northern Territory cattleman and his city nurse celebrated their engagement at the Kimberley Hotel, Halls Creek, and were subsequently married at St Mary's Cathedral in Sydney.

In a red Bedford truck loaded with six tea-chests of wedding presents we drove for days and days and days to our new home, a bough shed on the banks of a dry creekbed. How could there have been any signposts for this new bride? There wasn't a coil of wire let alone a fence; no building, no herd of cattle. Nonetheless, knowing that our love would make all things possible, I was undeterred by the challenges of building and developing our own cattle station from scratch, far removed from the rest of the world.

Of course I could not see around corners, anticipate the heartaches and hardships, or the victories and joys. There are no words to describe our anguish and grief when we lost our first-born son, Martin, to leukaemia when he was just nine months old. Yet somehow, somehow, as the years unfolded and other beautiful babies, schoolbooks, paddocks and fence lines merged, I managed to find my place in that new world, ever mindful, though, of the words of pioneer Patrick Durack: 'Cattle Kings ye call us? Then we are Kings in Grass Castles that may be blown away upon a puff of wind.'

When Marie and Patrick were born just twelve months apart in age, they seldom had interaction with any other children in our neighbourhood that extended for hundreds of kilometres. Their big adventures included sharing the saddle or tractor seat with John. Playmates were cuddly, crawling puppies, leaping grasshoppers, assorted moths, beautiful butterflies and all things of the earth. When Michael and Rebecca arrived to double our offspring, their elder sister and brother became devoted second parents. Life was never busier, noisier or more fulfilling for the six of us.

From infancy our little ones contributed to the development of our cattle station home during those crucial foundation years. Chubby little fingers helped plant trees and lawn and keen eyes followed tracks and weather patterns. As they learned to speak on the two-way radio and change a tyre almost before they could walk, their childhood was, in a way, an apprenticeship. It was all about survival – it is still all about survival. They reared poddy calves and handled responsibility with a maturity well beyond their years and always with much love and laughter.

Indelibly ingrained are our numerous steps and stairs. Upon arrival I was not unduly concerned that I did not have a house, or a homestead, as they called it, but anxiously inquired when I could expect my telephone. It was thirteen years before we graduated from the Royal Flying Doctor two-way radio communication system to a radio telephone. Even though that was cumbersome, it signified dramatic progress. With a degree of trepidation I became Teacher–Mum in our thoughtfully constructed home schoolroom. For eighteen years, correspondence lessons in conjunction with Katherine School of the Air afforded Marie, Patrick, Michael and Rebecca an excellent primary education. The dreaded interstate boarding school wrench broke all of our hearts, and yet we did our best to live by my mother's philosophy: 'What can't be cured must be endured.'

I remember the relief and elation when, after an eternal decade, Riveren became a separate lease from John's adjoining family-owned property, and the Riveren brand was struck – JUT. How appropriate, I mused – John Underwood and Terry. Wrong! It stood for John Underwood Territory – the latter being a compulsory requirement in the Northern Territory at the time.

These were the pillars of progress that revolutionised the life of one wife, mother and aspiring cattlewoman totally focused on conquering the challenges of coping 600 kilometres from town.

Surrounded by battlers and toilers intent on caring for their land, livestock and each other, I gradually developed an insight into, and an ever-increasing admiration and respect for, my new homeland and its people. They were a breed apart: resourceful, resilient, fiercely independent and content with their lot. As a spiritual reverence enveloped me, I felt increasingly compelled to take the bush to the rest of the world. One day I bought a new camera and the first of thousands of rolls of film. My camera became an extension of me, and from stockyards and helicopters I captured ordinary and extraordinary everyday images of life in the back of beyond. Eventually I selected the best, named my collection and arranged exhibitions.

The positive response to my photographic collection intensified throughout my solo exhibitions in Darwin in the Northern Territory, Rockhampton in Queensland and Sydney in New South Wales. The diverse images have been largely captured on my 3000-square-kilometre cattle station home, Riveren, photographs that reveal who we are and what we do and portray with understanding and poignant simplicity the essence of the Outback.

Somehow, somewhere, at some stage, I had magically become an insider.

The story of my transition from a city nurse to a bush bird in isolation has been encapsulated in my autobiography, *In the Middle of Nowhere*. The amazing response from my readers continues. Telephone calls, facsimiles and hundreds upon hundreds of letters acknowledge with gratitude and elation our story. Moreover, there is an outpouring of common emotions and experiences: 'Thank you for taking me on roads where there are no roads. I've laughed and cried with you over and over again. I even cried in the happy parts. No story has ever affected my family and me like this. When may we expect your next book?'

The ongoing intrigue and hunger deserve a response.

There has been mystique and romance associated with the Australian bush since time immemorial. Poets, writers and artists have for two centuries paid tribute to the dauntless and courageous pioneers whose remarkable exploits have made it possible for us to follow in their footsteps. From fact and folklore heroes and heroines have emerged, sometimes larger than life. Where else in the world has the Swagman, the Bushranger, the Shearer, Overlander and Drover been immortalised? In song and on the big screen, due tribute has been paid to 'the bushmen [who] love hard riding where the wild bush horses are' (A.B. Paterson, 'The Man from Snowy River'). Surely every Australian knows the words of our unofficial national anthem, 'Waltzing Matilda'.

However, there are schoolchildren today who think cotton comes from cows and believe there is no need for farmers and graziers any more as we can import our food from overseas. Right now the rural population is sadly in decline. Many rural towns are dying and the negatives multiply. Banks continue to foreclose, decimating families who have honoured their heritage over many generations. There is an increasing sense of despondency, despair and disrepair in the bush as the haemorrhaging of rural Australia continues. The hurt must be lessened and the haemorrhaging arrested. It is time to sharply focus the spotlight on the little-known Australia, which is historically the backbone of our nation.

As cattle families continue to work the inland of Australia, the challenges to survive have never been greater. The Northern Territory is still in a sense the last frontier. However, it is also the gateway to Asia. Against all odds, including the vagaries of nature and the unpredictability of markets, we contribute to the economy of our mighty nation. We have had to embrace change and grasp every opportunity. Armed with renewed knowledge and greater courage and determination than ever before, we are thinking and competing globally.

As we enter the new millennium, we must keep the camp fires of our history glowing. If we allow them to go out, will they ever be relit? It is also imperative to share images of modern-day pioneers, who all too quickly will become part of history. I believe this book will play a vital role in enticing new generations to a life beyond the bitumen, to a demanding yet satisfying existence in the land where the spell of the Never Never still bewitches the unsuspecting. As we examine and acclaim what it really means to be Australian, this message of hope and promise cannot be ignored.

From bough shed beginnings thirty-two years ago, Riveren has now been documented as one of the best-developed pastoral properties in the Northern Territory. Seven sets of permanent stockyards linked by laneways and the ongoing creation of additional paddocks and man-made watering points have resulted in a fully productive enterprise run by a small, efficient team.

Michael's full-time and long-term commitment to home and industry has relieved John of significant physical pressures. The sole pilot of our Robinson 22 helicopter, Michael achieves the outcomes of several stockmen as he musters and accesses all year round every far-flung corner of our station.

John continues to regularly fly our Cessna 182 aircraft, and between these two knowledgeable pilots a constant, intimate and critical overview of cattle and country is maintained. An extraordinarily capable all-rounder, John is the data base whose work ethic inspires and influences all who know him. Recently John's agri-political endeavours and service to primary industry, particularly the cattle industry, and to the community were recognised in the 1998 Queen's Birthday Honours. We are all so proud of John's appointment as a Member of the Order of Australia in the General Division.

As often as possible Marie returns from her Paspaley Pearls work base in Darwin, seemingly a suburb of Riveren, to contribute her inborn skills. She excels equally in the kitchen, paddock and stockyards and loves nothing greater than to inspect newborn calves and foals as their parental old friends are greeted with mutual affection.

Patrick, having just returned from his world-wide year-long pilgrimage, participates with ease in our diverse daily activities before springboarding back to accountancy employment in our capital city. His sound economic advice would otherwise be unavailable.

Rebecca's final university holidays are hardly long enough for her to wean all the stud paddocks, update the computer records and generally inspect our entire herd. Like Michael, her pregnancy testing and artificial insemination skills are in constant demand. It is exciting to have an agricultural scientist in our family.

Marie, Patrick, Michael and Rebecca, all of whom have bush souls, reflect their grass-roots upbringing, each displaying resilience, integrity, loyalty and an attachment to home that defies definition.

Over the years we infused Brahman bloodlines into our Shorthorn nucleus herd. Today we all contribute to the ongoing necessary upgrade of our bloodlines, in order to continue to produce the highly sought-after Brahman beast for the live export trade. After the currency crisis and Asian meltdown two years ago, our ever-changing overseas markets are once again buoyant.

Journey with me through my beloved Riveren. These glimpses, afforded to too few and unrecognised by those who create them, are for you.

Eagle's eye stalks, dingo's eye blinks,
Newborn calf peeps, blood red sun winks,
Cattleman's eye gazes, mother's eyes guard and love,
How superbly eye of camera has captured the above.

HELICOPTER RINGER

Like his father, Michael has had the advantage of gaining maximum experience mustering on horseback before taking to the skies. From his manoeuvrable Robinson 22, he can handle vast distances to work scattered cattle into a single mob. In large areas, the helicopter ringer can do the work of ten horseback musterers. Always done within personal and machine limitations, aerial mustering requires intense concentration.

BEST FRIENDS

Today Whitney, who has now had six calves, remains as gentle and loving and welcoming as this moment when she nuzzled Becky's hair and wanted to stay beside her forever.

WILD DOG DINGO

From the fast-flying helicopter it is possible to keep abreast with the fleet-footed dog — both Hunter and Hunted.

Although he is camouflaged by Dry Season grasses and foliage, cattle are instinctively alert to his presence. Many a cow has tenaciously fought this predator. With swinging head she will protect her calf against one dog or more. He travels solo or in a pack. Throughout the night and in particular at daybreak, the chilling howls of wild dog dingo cut the stillness, in prelude to the predictable bird orchestra.

BUDGIE BAR

A huge flock of bright-green budgerigars form an ever-changing cloud above the turkey nest, the bar of the bush to these exquisite creatures. In vast arid areas, these tiny bush birds must drink water daily to survive. As though in orbit, some swiftly swoop to drink momentarily before regrouping amidst feathered friends, twittering boisterously as they await their turn. Their volume is astonishing, as are their law and order, governed by a factor unknown.

FREEDOM

This sure-footed, unbroken colt gallops effortlessly across the plain with a great sense of wellbeing and zest for life.

'And God took a handful of southerly wind, blew His breath over it and created the horse.'

BEDOUIN LEGEND

EMU FAMILY

It is not uncommon to see emus moving in scorching midday temperatures. They are, however, uncommon at Riveren. Long powerful legs enable them to outpace predators, as they are capable of maintaining a speed of fifty kilometres per hour for more than one kilometre. After the female lays the eggs, the male is responsible for the young chicks for as long as eighteen months. This giant flightless bird of very ancient lineage is revered in Aboriginal Dreamtime. It is a well-recognised bird, standing on our coat of arms with the kangaroo.

CHAPTER TWO

The Country, Elements and Seasons

The power of the man and his land touched my soul

Our cattle station is larger than Luxembourg or the Australian Capital Territory. Riveren sprawls across the headwaters of the historic Victoria River, which meanders 800 kilometres to the Timor Sea. The river proved a monumental challenge to Augustus Charles Gregory. In 1855 he and his party set out to examine the source of the Victoria River and surrounding country and, in doing so, prove or dispel the suspicions of all explorers of the day – that an inland sea existed in the centre of Australia.

In following the course of the Victoria, Gregory naturally ended up on Riveren. Continuing west towards Inverway, John's family property, he identified the watershed as approximately 1600 feet above sea level (just over 500 metres), where the waters run off in all directions. The Negri and Stirling Rivers run north into the Ord River. Gregory followed Sturt Creek south-west across the West Australian border, then south to Gregory's Salt Sea (now called Lake Gregory) in the Great Sandy Desert.

During my novitiate years John explained these river systems on the occasions when we would pull up to change a flat tyre, then linger to boil the billy, thereby affording us the opportunity to look around in wonderment from that same plateau visited so long ago by the leader of the North Australian Expedition.

Our remarkable early explorers traversed inhospitable country against unimaginable adversities to charter the unknown vastness of Australia, the driest, flattest and lowest continent on earth.

With more than one-third of the total area of the Northern Territory being arid, the entire Red Centre is sometimes misconceived as Australia's 'Dead Heart'. Here the giver of light, energy and heat, the most powerful influence over our weather, seems to work overtime. It can become a sun-scorched country, as parched as its creatures are pitiful.

We are certainly at the mercy of the elements. Drought, cyclones, hail and floods can cause heavy and often crippling losses of land, livestock and investment. Within the starkness of my own back yard, I have, in addition, witnessed lightning strikes, choking dust storms, ravaging bushfires and earth tremors, the fearsome effects of which are blatantly accentuated by our isolation. Is it any surprise then that eyebrows instantly raise when I state that Riveren is very sweet country, providing it rains? If in favour with Mother Nature, our pastoral property becomes a fertile paradise, where cattle and horses thrive.

Relocating to Riveren required many adjustments, not the least being the dramatic reduction in seasons. I had to exchange the four traditional seasons for two – the Wet and the Dry.

In October, temperatures in excess of 40 degrees Celsius are common as the build-up to the Wet Season commences. Surface waters for livestock are checked vigilantly. People, too, consume even greater quantities of water as sweating soaks and saturates the protective clothing so necessary in the tropics. However, there is more focus on the excitement of the build-up and the long-awaited outcomes than on physical discomfort. There has never been room for self-indulgence in this land of never-ending space and freedom.

The senses run riot in our complex but uncluttered atmosphere. Attuned eyes monitor lonely wisps of cloud-forming cirrus. Convective clouds either tease and disintegrate or hopefully burgeon into threatening cumulonimbus. How deliriously we react to the first tantalising smell of rain on rising winds, swiftly followed by audible plops that suddenly accelerate to bombard tin rooftops with deafening rhythm. Rumbling, grumbling thunder crashes in league with terrifying lightning flashes to ensure a prolonged performance. Water is life.

Throughout the Wet the oppressive heat remains at fever pitch. The toilet seat is hot and gloves are worn to work with steel. The coolest water is tepid. As soaring temperatures sear the earth and its inhabitants, the flora looks singed. At times tempers fray. In towns there is talk of those who have contracted Mango Madness or Gone Troppo in another Silly Season.

Hopefully, tropical storms and monsoon influences provide ongoing rains for approximately six months, to run creeks and rivers and transform withering, dreary herbage into nutritious grasses. These follow-up rains create a miraculous revival, as calves and foals and other creatures galore gambol and gallop, scurry and scuffle, bucking and playing in a landscape as green as the Emerald Isle. Perennial Mitchell and annual Flinders grasses are interspersed with a profusion of wildflowers of every hue, adding new variety to the luxurious rich tapestry.

We then look forward to a productive Dry Season, which officially commences in May. As cooler months unfold the grasses hay off, and beneath cloudless, brilliant blue skies cattle mustering commences. Another season is under way in a new world.

ETCHINGS

As the giant bumble bee dips and darts, hovers and hunts, I'm exhilarated by the bird's-eye view from the cabin of our Robinson 22 helicopter. From the moment of lift-off the thrill never wanes. Cocooned within the perspex bubble and secured by seatbelts, my hair wildly whips and stings my face as I hastily change another roll of film.

Michael's piloting skills, combined with his knowledge of livestock and our country, make him a top mustering pilot. He monitors and controls cattle forming a discernible line beside the parallel road and snaking gully as they string into McKenzie Yards. Black-soil plains are flush with much-favoured Mitchell grass. With the world literally at our feet, we appreciate all over again the precious natural resources of our country.

WONDROUS WET SEASON

Spectacular blues and purples rumble and roar above glorious greens and golds.
The blaze of wildflowers is interspersed by a scattering of Brahmans grazing beneath
brooding skies. Undisturbed by the turbulence overhead, mother and calf bask in the
last stab of sunlight minutes before three inches of torrential rain instantly blot out
everything, the wet blackness drenching the grass-covered country.

MUSTERING MUCCA AFTER THE WET

After a generous Wet Season, historic Mucca Waterhole is full. Cattle swim effortlessly, following their leader, while the hovering helicopter ensures there is no turning back. Strategically positioned on the far bank, Michael is today on horseback, awaiting the other stockman at the tail of the mob. The two on horseback are the last to cross the river.

DUSTY TRACK

Sometimes dust hangs in the air like a thick pall; other times brisk winds swirl minute particles before sending it on its way. Irrespective of conditions, the Aboriginal stockman on the tail of the mob pauses to ensure there are no stragglers. His keen eyesight and natural instinct make him the right man in the right place.

SMOKO

It's always best when it's a family affair. Members of our most reliable workforce are forever willing and available. Their passionate love of home is obvious as, over damper and billy tea, Michael, John, Becky and Patrick contemplate the condition of the cattle and country at Inde Hole, hoping for imminent signs of an early Wet Season. They have grown up learning a little more each day about every aspect of running a station. Each individual is multi-skilled and these skills complement and interconnect, ensuring a successful outcome to every venture.

FRIEND OR FOE

Fire has been used for centuries as an effective tool. Control burning is carried out routinely in certain areas, taking into consideration land type, pasture composition and growth. Some bushfires, started by lightning strikes and fanned by boisterous winds, can burn unchecked for days and weeks. Graded roads make natural fire breaks around buildings and other relevant areas.

WATER ON THE ROCKS

On Riveren, the Victoria River only runs for several months of the year before
drying back to waterholes like this semi-permanent one at Inde Hole. Patrick guzzles
the most thirst-quenching liquid of all on his way out to Neave Bore on a routine bore
run. He will drop off supplementary lick blocks in the breeder paddocks further out.
During the Wet, blocks high in phosphorus are fed, while during the Dry, blocks
high in urea are used. Urea stimulates the bugs in the rumen to better utilise
dry feed for energy and nutrition.

GOOD TIMES

During prolonged drought this scene would be devoid of grass. After fire it would be black and bare. Today the countryside is in good order with an abundant supply of standing hay. As settled cattle graze contentedly, it is a sight to behold.

BUSH FILLIES

Uninhibited and unafraid, females young and not so young enjoy the aftermath of an early storm. Little Hannah is visiting from her Kimberley cattle station. Hooves and bare feet explore freshly laid puddles with delight. Innocence and trust abound.

CHAPTER THREE

The Harmony of the Land and Its Inhabitants

*I sensed their powerful bond, an invisible cord of respect
and instinct and co-ordination between each other, and between man
and beast as night and day merged and the stock work continued*

The cadence of Condamine bells is silent. Across the vast cattle runs of northern Australia, the largest in the world, the composition of the cattle team has altered. In recent decades, dramatic changes have engulfed us all, and those who have resisted have not survived. Today, in conjunction with aerial mustering, a small, multi-skilled workforce operates efficiently and effectively these pastoral properties. Only unchangeable are the independence and dependence of people and animals in this land beyond time.

On one of my first visits to this country thirty-five years ago, I was privileged to visit John's stockcamp, where he and twenty Aboriginal stockmen worked from sun up until sun down. Daily they defied danger as they flushed out cattle from hills and scrub, across treacherous gullies and punctuated plains. Irrespective of race and age, they worked as a team. They were successful because they knew the country, trusted their spirited mounts and understood their cattle. Theirs was a powerful connection to Mother Earth.

Around the glowing stockcamp fires we squatted and sprawled at day's end, swapping yarns and planning tomorrow in the spacious stockman's office. Beneath skies illuminated by billions of God's twinkling candles, the weary unrolled their swags, the most basic and welcoming of beds, even to the city tourist. The rostered few took turns on night watch, singing as they rode around the mustered mob. The songs they sang kept themselves awake and the cattle settled. Cattle are easily spooked and a rush was to be avoided at all costs.

As the plaintive call of the curlew shattered the stillness of piccaninny daylight, the old camp cook prepared nourishing tucker with minimum ingredients and fuss. Beef, damper and golden syrup, washed down by scalding sweet billy tea, formed the staple stockcamp diet. How I longed to ride beside the horse tailer. With an offsider, he would usher his large plant of horses, one hundred or more, across immeasurable unfenced distances to each camp. Packhorses and mules carried cooking utensils, food rations and assorted gear. In earlier times camels too were used as beasts of burden. Those days have all too quickly faded into oblivion.

Plunging way back again to the mid-nineteenth century, Australia was then long considered an empty continent, and there were horrifying stories of cruel defeat and destruction by those who endeavoured to open up the North. It was fourth time lucky for one of our most courageous pathfinders. On 24 July 1862, after four long years and a ride of 10,000 miles, John McDouall Stuart became the first explorer to reach the geographical centre of the Australian continent as he successfully crossed from south to north. His favourite mare, Polly, valiantly toiled beneath or beside him, both man and beast emerging from death's door many times over. Their bond of devotion and affection has been relived by countless others since. Blind and ill, Stuart did not claim his reward of 200,000 square miles of country; however, his legacy beckoned future generations. In his journal he recorded: 'If this country is settled, it will be one of the finest Colonies under the Crown, suitable for the growth of any and everything.'

The following year the Territory was annexed to South Australia, confirming faith in the future of the North. Twelve months later still, the man whose name is perpetuated in the 1600-kilometre bitumen highway from Alice Springs to Darwin died an old man at fifty.

Stories of yesteryear have a profound effect on present-day people. Nothing is ever taken for granted. The spiritual connection to the land of Australia's original inhabitants is shared by us all. For years Aboriginal stockmen and stockwomen have ridden beside their whitefella counterparts, without clash of culture or conflict. The common bond is our empathy with the land. From hunters and gatherers to early pioneering families to the Riveren team of today, subsistence depends on the land. With unwavering commitment and an invigorated environmental awareness, we care for our country, our creatures and each other. We are one.

I have learned incalculable lessons from the animal kingdom. By their very predictability, these creatures of habit often indicate stress or illness if the pattern changes. In the early morning, Brahmans graze as they head purposefully towards their watering point. By smoko time, they have watered. In closely scattered groups around the trough, they lie and rest for hours. It seems a carefully constructed exposition, as they loudly exhale or moan or snore, like tenors and baritones in an atmosphere that enhances the unusual musical score. Beside contented cows, milk-filled calves stretch, unable to keep their long-lashed, hooded eyes open. Even the massive majestic bulls relax, having risen to the occasion and fulfilled their instinctive duties. And so the cycle of life continues all around those of us who are favoured witnesses.

ARE YOU ALL RIGHT?

From a very young age Becky kept detailed cattle records in her amazing memory and stud records on paper prior to our computer acquisition. On this occasion years ago in Back Paddock, Becky, feeling relaxed and a little sleepy, lay down unhampered, unafraid and totally at ease. Her puzzled Brahman heifer and bull calf companions move to inspect one of their favourite friends in this strange position. Damp noses touch warm skin with reassurance.

INVERWAY WOMEN

They have never seen a city: shy, silent and sensitive indigenous women. Poppy, who used to live at Riveren, has now retired to neighbouring Inverway Station, John's former home. Patient and placid, she and Trixie are undeterred by old Nanny's insatiable appetite. The sole survivor of a once substantial goat herd, Nanny lives slightly apart from the numerous assortment of pet dogs, who are well used to her presence.

TWO PLUS ONE

They work tirelessly side by side, day in and day out. Snaps loyally shadows her master, Scott, who reflects on the day's activities with Albert. There are no boundaries or barriers between those committed to this life of hardships and pleasures and the sense of freedom they cherish.

READY TO RIDE

There are no traffic lights or congested highways in the middle of nowhere. Having caught their horses without delay, the four keen young stockmen lead them over to their saddles. Mick, Frank, Scott and Dave are about to muster Revolver Paddock.

DINNER CAMP

Curious cattle epitomise the sought-after Brahman temperament as, at close quarters, they observe members of the boardroom of the bush. Many important discussions take place as the billy boils, often when the sun is at its zenith. The horses are on standby in case the cattle wander.

IN THE SWAG

Although camping out is no longer a regular part of life in the Riveren stockcamp, the experience is still relished by those of us who embrace the great outdoors and glorious star-studded Outback skies. As a pup, Biddy loathed missing out on anything and became bodyguard in turn for various family members. With one or both eyes open as the noises of the night tease and torment the young blue heeler, Biddy remains intent on protecting Patrick.

MAGIC

Horse breeding, like cattle breeding, requires careful planning and selection of bloodlines. We have formed a new alliance since Neolithic man's primeval dependence on the horse as a food source. Framed by his parents, this cheeky, thoroughly irresistible foal knows no fear.

CATTLEMEN'S EYES GAZE

Another day, another yarding. The visiting South African and the Riveren stockman observe the cattle to be trucked. They recognise individual beasts because cattle are as different as people. Their thoughts turn to weights of the mob as they plan the loading.

LET'S GO

Despite December scorching temperatures and rocky terrain, Winner and Bevo,
two mates from down south, have survived an arduous day of fencing. On the way
home, Patrick and Michael share the historic and inspirational Buchanan Yards.
They talk about all challenges being relevant.

RIDING OUT

There is no threat of monotony as keen horsemen on smart stock horses leave the yards to muster Ridge Paddock. Beneath the borrowed cap is a visitor from a South African farm, gratefully absorbing this work-experience opportunity. It's a life worthwhile out here in uncluttered spaces, a long way away from the rush and crush of the cantankerous city.

YARDS AHEAD

Cold easterlies have abated as shadows shrink. The mustered mob string out in the laneway, which feeds them unwittingly into the yawning gates of the stockyards. Educated horses are undisturbed by the chopper, which remains in charge until the gates are closed behind the last beast. From my privileged position I sense the relief of the pilot beside me. The muster has gone well, but the day is just a pup. Michael will soon land, then take up his position in the yards.

MUCCA YARDS

On this second round of mustering in August, the weather is kind, although noise and dust abound. These permanent steel stockyards servicing surrounding paddocks are located seventeen kilometres east of our homestead. They are designed to facilitate the sorting of cattle into groups. The mustered mob will be moved through the yards to the 'pound' (swinging gates giving a five-way draft), where they are drafted accordingly: weaners one way, calves towards the calf cradle for branding, while bulls and cows are directed into other yards.

AFTER THE MUSTER

Water droplets sparkle in the brilliant sunlight as sweaty horses enjoy a well-earned wash down. My visit to the all-female stockcamp at Pigeon Hole, an outstation of Victoria River Downs, afforded me the opportunity to witness diligent stockwomen proving that gender need not be an issue.

CALF BRANDING

Gas furnaces have long ago replaced open fires and fire drums for heating branding irons. The calf cradle immobilises the calf as the brand of identification and proof of ownership is applied. As horns are dangerous and can cause extensive bruising, all animals are dehorned at this point.

Just as weaning is an important management tool, so too is 'mothering up'. It is important to ensure that all calves are then reunited with their mothers.

BLOOD RED SUN WINKS

Bushfire smoke and blistering heat combine to mask and distort surroundings. The fiery sun spills over faraway horizons as dust from the occupied stockyards contributes to the weird blur across the vastness of this ever-changing land.

STEADY

Weaner management sets the pattern for the rest of the animals' lives. Against a backdrop of red laterite hills, a capable young stockman leads weaners towards the stockyards. His intelligent horse, Biscuit, is also on a mission to keep the youngsters under control. The unbroken line of cattle reflects the trust of the mob as they hear Dave rhythmically murmur: 'Steady. Steady.'

These are the skills of the cattleman, unknown to any but those to whom they are ingrained.

LET THEM COME

During the early 1960s, drovers were largely replaced by road trains, and today road transportation of cattle is big business. The ramps are down and gates open. As nimble as a tightrope performer, the truckie crosses the catwalk, yelling that everything is in order to load the cattle.

HOW MANY THERE?

Gone are the days of four- to five-year-old fat bullocks being our turn-off or sale animals. Steers between 340–380 kilogram live weight fit the exporter's contract. The cattle are counted onto the truck with twenty-eight head to each deck or compartment.
'Him and his mate; him and his mate.' Albert and Scott count individually and a total of 280 head is confirmed.

ON THE MOVE

His cabin is his home for most of the season. The truckie's personal interest in his passengers is paramount. Loaded double-decker road trains, ten decks in all, leave the homestead yards. After the way bills or travel documents are completed, the trucks commence their 1000-kilometre haul to the export yards near the Darwin wharf.

THE INEVITABLE

All male horses can't be stallions. Michael reassures the young colt about to be branded and castrated.

CHAPTER FIVE

Faltering Footsteps and Enriching Friendships

People who think animals are replaceable are wrong

In a land where mirages mischievously distort reality and water evaporates before one's eyes in long, hot, dry spells, I have faced truth and cried oceans of tears.

When Becky left Riveren, not just her home but her entire world, to embark on her boarding school journey, I crumpled. All my children were gone. Over the years the ache of emptiness does not lessen; the gnaw of fear for their safety remains. Amongst my multitude of distractions, poddy calves are the best. Recently John discovered a special case and when I saw the deeply gouged thigh and ripped ears of the beautiful wide-eyed calf, I knew it would be difficult to save this orphan. It was Mother's Day.

Biddy and Texan, two blue heelers, could probably smell the dingo scent, for they sniffed and licked their welcome even more vigorously than usual. Our cattle dogs fearlessly guard and defend their human family and animal friends from their wild red counterparts, which are despised for their cruelty and cunning. In anticipation of frothy bubbles from the calf's mouth, a drooling overweight Biddy watched me prepare Denkavit. As I patiently urged the newest poddy to accept the black rubber teat, the calf suddenly and miraculously sucked. All the while Texan gently and thoroughly licked and cleansed the ugly wounds until her 'patient' slept safely beneath a sheltering bloodwood tree.

In time the honey-coloured calf grew in strength and, as trusty Texan persisted with her wound care, healing progressed remarkably well. Mums integrated with some older poddy graduates, whose size and confidence found them heading further out to feed. Boldly and bravely they eventually camped out overnight, although I watched anxiously each morning for their return. Noisily they would run down the road, leaping the house grid like well-rehearsed acrobats, then jostle for teats around the cafeteria as I filled it with Denkavit.

One morning only seven returned and I knew instantly who was missing: the youngest and weakest – Mums, Splodge, Little Red and Roger. It did not take me long on my drive around House Paddock to find two freshly killed bodies, but, although I tracked and criss-crossed methodically, I could not locate the other two. I wept in anger, frustration and sadness. Wretched dingoes had killed my four poddy calves for sport.

The control of feral animals is an integral part of responsible management and as soon as possible we organised our routine supervised dingo-baiting programme. Of necessity every care is taken and the sign on the boundary gate informs visitors that this property has had 1080 baits recently laid. No one saw Texan disappear. She was there one night and missing next morning. Despite detailed and extensive searching on the ground and in the helicopter, Michael could find no trace or clue. For days we all looked for the dear little dog so loyal and true, who never ventured or strayed from the homestead. Misery and irony ruled. We never found her remains to bury the little life-saver beside her predecessors in this country of mystery and camouflage.

Thérèse always had a mind of her own. Beautifully built, she typifies the Brahman breed – well proportioned, feminine and intelligent. Her show preparation put Becky on notice; however, Becky too has a mind of her own. Thérèse initially objected to halter, hose and handler equally, but prolonged persistence paid off and at length Becky paraded Thérèse before the Darwin and Katherine Show judges. She won! However, knowing her unpredictability, Big John was elected to lead Thérèse in the Grand Parade. Marie, Patrick, Michael, Becky and I all lead larger but more docile beasts. It was at the half-way mark that Thérèse yanked free and ran off with John in hot pursuit, spurred on by encouraging roars from the appreciative spectators.

With yet another newborn at foot, we checked Thérèse morning and evening. Hours became days and still the little heifer would not, could not, suck. Mother and calf were slowly escorted to the yards for feeding supervision. With mother immobilised in the bale, a calf will normally grasp the teats and gratefully and joyously drink its fill. This calf quickly earned its name Stupid. It nibbled and sucked every other part of its mother's lower anatomy and required human guidance over and over again.

They were a trying pair but well worth every effort and the battle for survival. Today Stupid is big and strong and as quiet as any poddy calf. Cattle never forget, and those handled when young always respond to people. Even an aged cow, a breeder many times over, or a fully grown working bull will move towards a vehicle or recognised individuals to exchange greetings. This is a country where friendships are unconditional.

CHEEK TO CHEEK

Closer than close are friends whose communication is only understood by these three. Their gentle honey hues blend and permeate before the stark steel stockyards, solitary witness to this spellbinding encounter.

COOLING OFF

The dogs could be forgiven for momentarily thinking Becky was back home when cousin Nicole came to visit. Panting Precious reckons the trough is not big enough for everyone. When her friends jump out, she will jump in.

TWO OF A KIND

When Jerome could no longer rise to meet and greet John, his human equivalent sire and king, our favourite bull was sadly farewelled by us all. Unashamedly, tears streaked suntanned faces, tears of gratitude for a wonderful friend of fourteen years. His legacy lives on.

BEST OF THE BEST

Many years and many more dollars have transpired since the introduction of Brahman bloodlines into our nucleus Shorthorn herd. You can feel the breath of these gorgeous pure-bred Brahman calves displaying sought-after qualities in cattle: consistency, curiosity, docility and intelligence. The proof is always in the progeny.

BELONGING

This family interaction was captured at the annual Katherine Show. Their extraordinary warmth and love are complemented by his dignity and her admiration of her grandfather. Ronnie Booth is the President of the Binjari Association, whose community is on the outskirts of Katherine. His hands have held horses' reins as he worked cattle and country for many years. Our common bonds afforded me the opportunity to present this magnetic portrait.

THE WHIPS

The might and power of the bush race horse is evident on the dusty dirt track at the Timber Creek annual races. Beating hearts press against heaving ribs. Distant roars from the encouraging crowd add a final spur to each rider and mount. Following two-up by twilight, the race ball commences with bush champagne — Bundy and Coke — flowing freely.

Once the solitary social event of the year, the bush race meeting still attracts a huge following of station people and town folk from far and wide. Even if one does not own a racehorse, the races present the perfect opportunity for families, friends and acquaintances, young and old, to catch up on events and compare notes from the previous year or last get-together.

THE FUTURE

Memories of droving treks, night watch and evening campfires where bush yarns emanated like drifting smoke remain vivid. He remembers his old mates, many of whom have already handed in their spurs to the Supreme Boss.

Women, who feed their families and the world, will continue to work beside their men. They will play an increasingly prominent role in meeting the challenges of sustainability and international prosperity.

A Kenyan proverb tells us: 'We do not inherit the earth from our ancestors; we borrow it from our children.'

FAMILY

The grandeur and fragility of our land are at the forefront of planning and appreciation. We inspected cattle at Hut Creek before turning our backs with barely suppressed glee on the rapidly approaching, long-awaited storm. It will be an exciting race home.

The family unit has never been more important. We are aware of the enormity of the task ahead.